SCIENCE PRACTICE EXERCISES
13+
Answer Book

Ron Pickering

www.galorepark.co.uk

Published by ISEB Publications, an imprint of Galore Park Publishing Ltd

19/21 Sayers Lane, Tenterden, Kent TN30 6BW
www.galorepark.co.uk

Design and typography Typetechnique

Printed by Replika Press, India

ISBN: 978 1 907047 47 3

First published 2010, reprinted 2011, 2011, 2012

Details of other ISEB publications and examination papers, and Galore Park publications are available at www.galorepark.co.uk

Contents

Introduction

Science Practice Exercises 13+ Answer Book provides a full set of answers to the questions in Science Practice Exercises 13+ by Ron Pickering, ISBN: 9781907047237 (Galore Park, 2010).

The mark scheme used in these books is in accordance with the ISEB marking criteria. Teachers and parents are advised to use their own discretion in judging whether a pupil has answered a question completely and accurately enough to be awarded full marks. A pupil may arrive at a unique answer not accounted for in this book, and these answers should not necessarily be discounted.

Ron Pickering
Summer 2010

Biology

1: Cells and organisation

1.1 (a) releasing energy (1)

   (b) getting rid of poisonous wastes (1)

   (c) sperm cell (1)

   (d) producing offspring (1)

   (e) taking in nutrients (1)

   (f) a cell (1)

   (g) secrete mucus (1)

   (h) a tissue (1)

   (i) root hair cell (1)

   (j) muscle cell (1)

1.2 (a) A (2)

   (b) cell wall; cilium; chloroplast (3)

1.3 (a) (i) A (1)
      (ii) to move particles of dust and microbes (1)

   (b) B (1)

   (c) C and E (2)

   (d) E (1)

1.4 (a) (i) chloroplast; cell wall (2)
      (ii) chloroplast (photosynthesis – to provide sugar for the plant)
      cell wall (to prevent the plant cell bursting) (2)
      (iii) A – membrane (to control what enters and leaves the cell);
      B – cytoplasm (place where chemical reactions occur inside the cell) (4)

   (b) (i) cells develop certain features that suit them to one particular function (1)
      (ii) red blood cell – transports oxygen – respiration
      nerve cell – carries impulses – coordination
      root hair cell – absorbs mineral ions – plant nutrition
      white blood cell – engulfs microbes – defence against disease
      egg cell – carries genes from female – reproduction (4)

1.5 (a) (i) chloroplast (1)

(ii) no photosynthesis takes place in roots (1)

(b) cell wall – helps keep cell shape
cell membrane – controls the entry and exit of substances
nucleus – contains the genetic material that controls the cell's activities
cytoplasm – many chemical reactions take place here
chloroplast – the site of the trapping of light for photosynthesis (5)

1.6 digestive – teeth and stomach
circulatory – heart
excretory – bladder
reproductive – testes
nervous – brain
breathing – lungs
skeletal – rib (9)

2: Nutrition and health

2.1 (a) protein   (1)

    (b) an enzyme   (1)

    (c) fibre   (1)

    (d) small intestine   (1)

    (e) starch   (1)

    (f) help develop strong bones   (1)

    (g) assimilation   (1)

    (h) iron   (1)

    (i) protein   (1)

    (j) incisors   (1)

2.2 (a) (i)   carbohydrate   (1)
          (ii) fat   (1)
          (iii) cheese   (1)

    (b) (i)   12 g   (1)
          (ii) water   (1)

    (c) (i)   1000 g/1 kg   (1)
          (ii) yes (95 g)   (1)

    (d) (i)   1000 mg (less than a pregnant woman requires, but more than a non-pregnant woman in order to provide calcium for the growing baby)   (1)
          (ii) she is still growing and producing bone and teeth   (1)
          (iii) to produce haemoglobin/red blood cells   (1)

2.3 (a) (i) E (1)

(ii) D (1)

(iii) in the bloodstream (1)

(b) (i) (4)

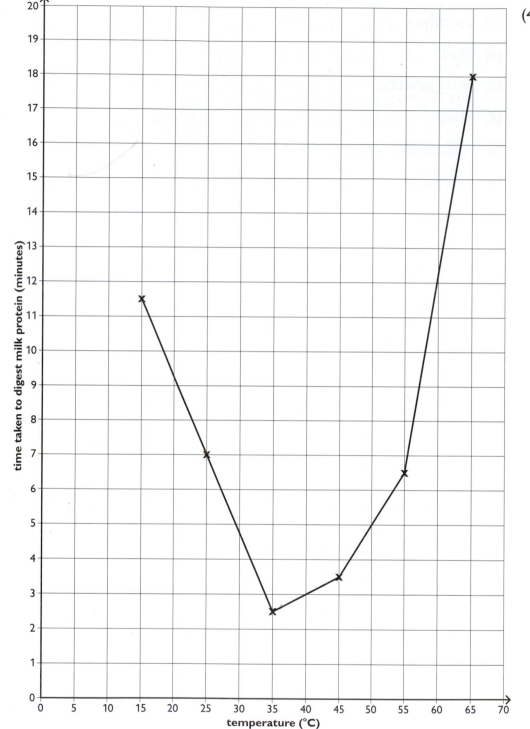

(ii) effect of temperature on digestion of milk protein (1)

(iii) 36.9 °C (1)

(iv) it is approximately the same temperature at which protein is digested fastest (1)

(v) Any two of:

concentration of milk

concentration of enzyme

distance between cross and test tube (2)

4

2.4 (a) too much salt – high blood pressure

too little iron – cannot carry enough oxygen in blood

too much fat – heart disease

not enough fibre – constipation

too little protein – slow growth of muscles (3)

(b) sugar – the main source of energy for working cells

calcium – required for development of bones and teeth

vitamin C – prevents scurvy

water – an important part of the process of digesting foods

starch – provides a slow, steady supply of sugar (3)

2.5 (i) (3)

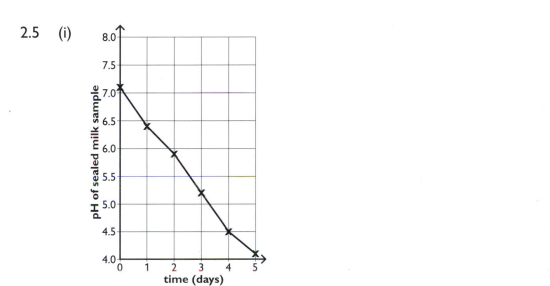

(ii) acid (lactic) (1)

(iii) 3.2 (1)

(iv) allow marks for any reasonable method, provided that the following variables are identified correctly:

temperature – independent variable

pH – dependent variable

time for reading and amount of milk – controlled variables (4)

(v) yoghurt or cheese (1)

(vi) keep the milk at a low temperature (bacteria will not multiply so quickly);

dry the milk and store it as granules (bacteria cannot multiply without water) (2)

3: Reproduction

3.1 (a) a sperm (1)

(b) 28 days (1)

(c) fertilisation (1)

(d) testis (1)

(e) nucleus (1)

(f) puberty (1)

(g) a zygote (1)

(h) placenta (1)

(i) hormones (1)

(j) gestation (1)

3.2 (a) (i) E (1)

(ii) D (1)

(iii) either A or B or both are acceptable answers (1)

(b) (i) sperm duct/vas deferens (C) (1)

(ii) the cut tube prevents sperm from being ejaculated so it cannot reach
the egg cell (1)

(c) (i) testis (1)

(ii) Any two of:
growth of facial hair
deepening voice
muscle development
pubic hair (2)

3.3 (a) (i)

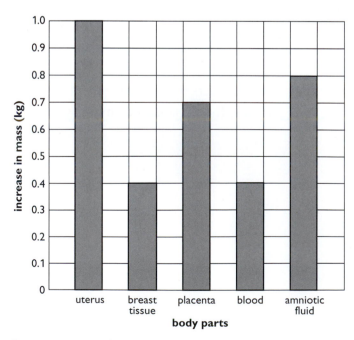

bars must not be touching and figure for fat must not be included (3)

6

(ii) 9 kg (1)

(iii) $0.7 \div 9.0 = 0.078$ to 0.08 (2)

(b) iron for red blood cells; calcium for bones and teeth (for developing fetus as well as for woman) (2)

(c) **nicotine** causes baby to have a faster heart rate, and baby can be born addicted to nicotine
carbon monoxide causes less oxygen to be carried by red blood cells so the baby can have slower respiration and less energy for growth (2)

3.4 (a) (i) sperm (1)

(ii) tail for swimming
nucleus carrying father's genes (2)

(b) (i) fertilisation (1)

(ii) in the oviduct (1)

(c) embryo; uterus; implantation/conception; placenta/umbilical cord (2)

3.5 (a) ovaries; month/28 days; menstruation; blood; period (3)

(b) (i) around day 13 to 15 (1)

(ii) days 1–4 (1)

(iii) days 14–17 (1)

3.6 (a) (i) D (1)

(ii) B (1)

(iii) C (1)

(b) protection against damage/drying out (1)

(c) An explanation should contain the following points in the correct order:
digested in small intestine → absorbed into blood → transported in blood across placenta and along umbilical cord (4)

(d) 9 months (1)

4: Respiration, energy and exercise

4.1   (a)   cartilage   (1)

      (b)   alveoli   (1)

      (c)   carbon dioxide   (1)

      (d)   red blood cells   (1)

      (e)   fingernails   (1)

      (f)   respiration   (1)

      (g)   green to red/orange   (1)

      (h)   tendon   (1)

      (i)   intercostals and diaphragm   (1)

      (j)   glucose   (1)

4.2   (a)   (i)   muscle   (1)
              (ii)   upwards and outwards   (1)

      (b)   heart; lungs   (2)

      (c)   (i)   triceps   (1)
              (ii)   biceps   (1)
              (iii)   antagonistic   (1)

      (d)   (i)   Any or all of the following:
                   to lubricate the joint
                   to prevent the joint from wearing
                   to prevent damage to the ends of bones   (1)
              (ii)   arthritis   (1)

4.3   (a)   (i)   1000 cm^3 (1)
              (ii)   20% of 1000 = 200 cm^3 per breath; there are 5 breaths in 10 seconds
                   so 1000 cm^3 every 10 seconds so 6000 cm^3 every minute   (4)
              (iii)   glucose + oxygen $\rightarrow$ carbon dioxide + water + energy   (2)

      (b)   the heart   (1)

      (c)   (i)   Q   (1)
              (ii)   P   (1)

4.4 (a) (i) type of food (1)
(ii) heat released, or the rise in temperature of water (1)
(iii) Any two of:
same mass of food
same volume of water
same temperature of surroundings (2)
(iv) A good answer would include at least two of:
can calculate means
results should be more reliable
less emphasis on one 'bad' result (2)

(b) (i) respiration (1)
(ii) Any two of:
growth
division of cells
movement
keep up body temperature (2)

4.5 (a) (i) B (1)
(ii) E (1)

(b) (i) tissue (1)
(ii) mucus traps bacteria and dust → cilia move bacteria and dust in mucus
up to mouth (2)
(iii) more mucus so 'coughing'
fewer cilia so mucus tends to slip back into lungs causing infection (2)

(c) (i) oxygen (1)
(ii) carbon dioxide (1)
(iii) diffusion (1)
(iv) thin lining means it is not far for gases to diffuse
large surface area means many gas particles can cross at the same time (2)

5: Health and disease

5.1   (a)   an antibody   (1)

      (b)   infectious   (1)

      (c)   athlete's foot   (1)

      (d)   wearing gloves when handling food   (1)

      (e)   a nucleus   (1)

      (f)   influenza   (1)

      (g)   liver damage   (1)

      (h)   meningitis   (1)

      (i)   an antibiotic   (1)

      (j)   constipation   (1)

5.2   (a)   more smoking increases risk of heart disease
risk increases with age (length of time smoking)   (2)

      (b)   (i)   A good answer should include:
less blood flow to heart muscle so less oxygen for respiration → heart muscle cells 'die' if they do not have enough energy from respiration   (2)

              (ii)   high blood pressure means delicate blood vessels are more likely to be damaged, and a person is at higher risk of a stroke   (1)

      (c)   (i)   needs cigarette approx every 100 minutes   (1)

              (ii)   no cigarettes whilst asleep   (1)

              (iii)   at 16 mg per litre of blood   (1)

              (iv)   will be reduced to approx 50 minutes   (1)

              (v)   nicotine patches   (1)

5.3   (a)   (i)   Any of: influenza/common cold/AIDS   (1)

              (ii)   Increase in antibodies is: faster; higher; lasts for longer   (3)

      (b)   A good answer should include: white blood cells and antibodies recognise virus by proteins on coat → virus is now 'camouflaged' → no signal for white blood cells   (2)

5.4   (a)   nerve impulses travel more slowly – reactions are slowed
blood vessels close to the skin open up – person looks red-faced
senses work less well – poor judgement of distance
liver cells try to remove alcohol from blood – long-term liver damage   (3)

(b) (i) alcohol is absorbed through the stomach and small intestine into
the mother's bloodstream and across the placenta to the fetus (3)
(ii) carbon monoxide causes less oxygen to be carried by red blood cells,
so respiration slows and there is less energy for growth (1)

5.5 (a) (i) less fat (reduced chance of heart disease/obesity)
less cholesterol (less heart disease)
more fibre (less colon cancer) (3)
(ii) has more protein for growth
more energy for exercise (2)

(b) (i) USA (1)
(ii) four times more likely (= 20 ÷ 5) (2)
(iii) wholemeal bread; apples (2)

5.6 (a) (i) bacteria take time to multiply to harmful levels (1)
(ii) bacteria killed by antibiotic so levels fall (1)
(iii) bacteria hadn't been killed completely so could multiply once again (1)

(b) (i) Any one of:
as part of blood plasma for transport
helps in digestion
part of fluid which lubricates joints (1)
(ii) acid removes enamel so inside of teeth exposed to decay (1)

(c) vaccine stimulates body's defences (makes antibodies) without actually
giving the person the disease (2)

6: Green plants as living organisms

6.1   (a)   carbon dioxide   (1)

      (b)   absorb minerals and water   (1)

      (c)   chloroplasts   (1)

      (d)   iodine solution   (1)

      (e)   cellulose   (1)

      (f)   stigma   (1)

      (g)   with gravity and away from light   (1)

      (h)   decomposers   (1)

      (i)   nitrate   (1)

      (j)   respires only, using oxygen   (1)

6.2   (a)   (i)   (4)

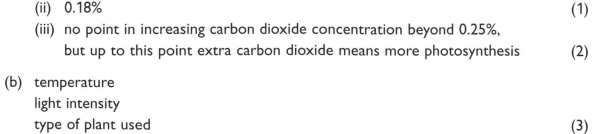

        (ii)   0.18%   (1)

        (iii)   no point in increasing carbon dioxide concentration beyond 0.25%,
            but up to this point extra carbon dioxide means more photosynthesis   (2)

      (b)   temperature
           light intensity
           type of plant used   (3)

(c) (i) oxygen relights a glowing splint (1)
    (ii) collect gas in an inverted measuring cylinder (1)
    (iii) repeat the experiment and use mean values (1)

6.3 (a) (i) chlorophyll (1)
    (ii) magnesium (1)
    (iii) to trap light energy for photosynthesis (1)

(b) pot has limited amount of compost so minerals are soon used up (1)

(c) (i) potassium – C; phosphate – D; nitrate – A; magnesium – B (2)
    (ii) Any two of:
        nitrates can increase growth of green algae which cut out light from
           other plants
        bacteria can use up oxygen in water
        fish die as the oxygen concentration in the water falls too low (2)
    (iii) Either of fungi or bacteria (1)

6.4 (a) (i) B (1)
    (ii) A (accept D) (1)
    (iii) G (accept E) (1)
    (iv) F (1)

(b) germinates; reproduction; pollination; fertilisation; dispersal (3)

(c) description should include the following steps:
    1. grind up seeds – wear safety goggles (safety precaution)
    2. suspend ground up seeds in water and then mix with iodine solution –
       don't get iodine solution on hands (safety precaution)
    3. look for blue-black colour; pure water should not react with iodine
       solution and iodine solution should not turn blue-black without mixing
       with starch suspension (controls) to demonstrate that no unknown variable
       is affecting the results, i.e. there is only a colour change if starch is
       definitely present (4)

6.5 (a) (i) carbon dioxide (1)
    (ii) yellow (1)
    (iii) snails are respiring and releasing carbon dioxide (1)

(b) (i) purple (1)
    (ii) carbon dioxide has been removed as plants photosynthesise (1)
    (iii) balance between respiration and photosynthesis (1)

(c) to show that indicator did not change colour without respiration or
photosynthesis (1)

7: Variation and classification

7.1   (a)   have three main body parts   (1)

      (b)   nucleus   (1)

      (c)   has no real roots or leaves   (1)

      (d)   fertilisation   (1)

      (e)   adaptation   (1)

      (f)   migration   (1)

      (g)   has a beak   (1)

      (h)   photosynthesise   (1)

      (i)   classification   (1)

      (j)   eye colour   (1)

7.2   (a)   (i)   ear size; presence or absence of spots   (2)
              (ii)   genes   (1)
              (iii)   sperm cell; egg cell   (2)

      (b)   (i)   type of diet   (1)
              (ii)   presence or absence of spots after 28 days   (1)
              (iii)   Any two of:
                   temperature
                   all other aspects of diet
                   how much light they received
                   gender of mice also acceptable   (2)

      (c)   genes only   (1)

7.3   (a)   type of skin
            whether or not it has a bony skeleton
            whether or not it has eyes   (3)

      (b)   spider – two body parts and eight jointed legs
            insect – three body parts and six jointed legs
            fungus – cells with a definite cell wall but no chlorophyll
            fern – produces spores and cells contain chlorophyll
            protist – body is made of a single cell, with a clear nucleus and cytoplasm   (5)

      (c)   (i)   the bacterial cell has no nucleus   (1)
              (ii)   a virus cannot carry out any life processes unless it is inside a living cell   (1)

7.4 (a) (2)

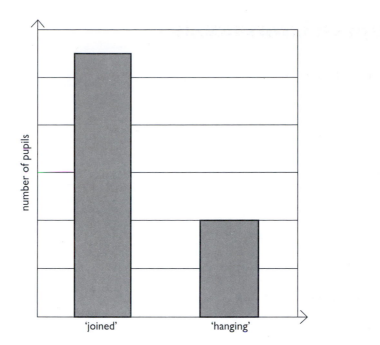

number of pupils

'joined'   'hanging'

(b) (i) otherwise results could not be compared with one another (1)

(ii) cm (1)

(iii) 3rd and 4th bars overlap, as do 4th and 5th bars (1)

(c) (2)

characteristic	inherited only	inherited and affected by the environment
shape of ear lobe	✓	
length of forearm		✓
ability to roll tongue	✓	

(d) (i) receives genes from both parents (so looks like them) but genes are a mixture of mother's and father's (so a 'mixture' of looks) (2)

(ii) they have been formed from a single zygote (so share the same set of genes from their parents) (1)

7.5 (a) otters can keep up their body temperature, so digestion provides more soluble foods, respiration provides energy and muscles are more flexible compared to the fish (3)

(b) (i) remain close to 40 °C, i.e. unchanged (1)

(ii) rise to 25 °C (1)

(c) (i) Any two of:
streamlined shape
webbed feet
long powerful tail (2)

(ii) feed their young on milk (1)

(iii) each has a backbone (they are vertebrates) (1)

(d) variation (1)

15

8: Ecology and environment

8.1 (a) decomposers   (1)

    (b) photosynthesis   (1)

    (c) a food chain   (1)

    (d) pesticide   (1)

    (e) quadrat   (1)

    (f) the original size of the population   (1)

    (g) an animal   (1)

    (h) woodland being cut down   (1)

    (i) 10%   (1)

    (j) predators   (1)

8.2 (a) (i) from bottom upwards: lettuce; snail; thrush; hawk   (1)
        (ii) wide bar at bottom of pyramid for parasites on thrush   (2)

    (b) fewer thrushes so number of snails likely to increase; more snails so
        more lettuces will be eaten   (2)

    (c) more nesting places so more babies; more possible foods so
        population will increase   (2)

8.3 (a) (i) they are equal   (1)
        (ii) curve is 'horizontal'   (1)

    (b) (i) C   (1)
        (ii) rate of increase begins to slow   (1)
        (iii) Any one of:
           presence of predators
           disease
           availability of oxygen in water
           pollution   (1)

    (c) (i) protein   (1)
        (ii) B
           B or C is also acceptable   (1)
        (iii) The best profit can be made by selling the fish just before population begins
           to level off. The population will continue to grow at the fastest rate,
           when some are caught.   (2)

8.4 (a) (i) a herbivore – krill/squid
a producer – phytoplankton
a carnivore – any organism other than phytoplankton, krill or bacteria
a decomposer – bacteria (4)

(ii) for example:
phytoplankton → krill → fish → Crabeater seal → Leopard seal (2)

(b) (i) animals eat many prey items, and mercury is not broken down so it
accumulates in the predator (1)

(ii) Leopard Seals are the top consumers so there are more steps to
concentrate the mercury (1)

(c) Any two of:
streamlined shape
webbed feet
sharp beak (2)

8.5 (a) no trees absorb water; water runs quickly off soil and downhill (1)

(b) Any two of:
fewer nesting sites
fewer chances to feed
fewer places to hide from predators (2)

(c) (i) fungi/bacteria (1)
(ii) respiration (1)
(iii)

(3)

(iv) so that there are equal numbers of males and females for sexual
reproduction (1)

(v) 33 °C (1)

8.6 nitrate – a mineral often added to farmland in fertilisers
     competition – two or more organisms are trying to obtain the same thing from
        their environment
     population – all of the members of the same species living in one area
     conservation – managing the environment for the benefit of wildlife   (4)

Chemistry

9: Experiments in chemistry

9.1   (a)   carbon dioxide   (1)

       (b)   from blue to pink   (1)

       (c)   hydrogen sulphide   (1)

       (d)   white to blue   (1)

       (e)   oxygen   (1)

       (f) $2.35 \ dm^3$ (1)

       (g)   deep blue   (1)

       (h)   an independent variable   (1)

       (i)   hydrogen   (1)

       (j)   pipette   (1)

9.2   (a)   (i)   measuring cylinder

                     beaker is also acceptable, but is less accurate   (1)

             (ii)   mm-ruled ruler   (1)

       (b)   (1)

                               (i) missing value added and points joined

                               (ii) rough values for candle 2 added and
                                      points joined

                                              (1)

       (c)   same wax

             same dimensions

             same distance between markings   (3)

9.3   (a)   (i)   to make sure that the hot vapour condensed to a liquid   (1)

             (ii)   carbon dioxide   (1)

             (iii)   The most obvious colourless liquid to test for is water. There are two
                       possible tests: either adding water to blue cobalt chloride will turn it pink
                       or adding water to white anhydrous copper sulphate will turn it blue.
                       These colour changes, in either cobalt chloride or copper sulphate,
                       demonstrate that the colourless liquid is water.   (2)

(b) (i) no naked flames; no drinking or eating (2)

(ii) the radiator could split (water expands as it freezes)

255 K is –18 °C

the concentration of antifreeze is 10% and this protects only to –5 °C (3)

9.4 (a) A – harmful; B – oxidising; C – corrosive; D – highly flammable; E – toxic (5)

(b) highly flammable; harmful; irritant (3)

9.5 (a) (i) hole open or closed (1)

(ii) heat released (time taken for water to boil) (1)

(b) the position of the Bunsen burner below the beaker; the volume of water in the beaker; the position of the gas tap (i.e. how much flow of gas) (3)

9.6 (5)

effect on limewater	pH with Universal Indicator	effect on a burning splint	gas
none	4	puts it out	sulphur dioxide
none	7	goes 'pop'	hydrogen
turns it cloudy	6	puts it out	carbon dioxide
none	7	burns more brightly	oxygen
none	8	puts it out	ammonia

9.7 (a) (i) mass of water = 196.4 g – 116.4 g = 80 g

density of water = 80 g ÷ 80 cm^3 = 1 g per cm^3

mass of alcohol = 180.2 g – 116.4 g = 63.8 g

density of alcohol = 63.8 g ÷ 79 cm^3 = 0.8 g per cm^3 (3)

(ii) pipette (1)

(b) (4)

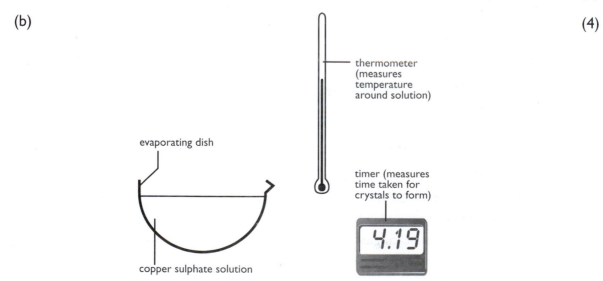

evaporating dish

thermometer (measures temperature around solution)

timer (measures time taken for crystals to form)

4.19

copper sulphate solution

20

10: Solids, liquids and gases

10.1 (a) vibrate more (1)

(b) freezes below 0 °C (1)

(c) evaporation (1)

(d) condensation (1)

(e) the input variable (1)

(f) diffusion (1)

(g) mass/volume (1)

(h) rise (1)

(i) boiling point (1)

(j) remains the same (1)

10.2 (a) (i) B (1)

(ii) temperature does not change as a substance changes state;
temperature of the wax did not change between points B and C (2)

(iii) liquid (1)

(b) Any two of:
readings can be taken more frequently (continuously)
can go away and leave readings being taken
likely to be more accurate (2)

(c) water bath is used so maximum temperature is 100 °C (boiling point
of water) (1)

(d) answer must refer to water and not to wax → water molecules moving more
rapidly at end of experiment → leave surface as they gain enough energy from
heat to evaporate away (2)

10.3 (a) (i) pressure falls as individual molecules have less energy to 'press' against
the surface area of the inside of the container (2)

(ii) likely to get smaller/weaker (1)

(iii) high temperature would increase pressure and can could explode (1)

(b) the same size as
closer together than
moving more slowly (3)

10.4 (a) (i) object size increases (1)

(ii) gaps get smaller (1)

(iii) concrete might fracture; bridge could buckle (1)

(b) so solid concrete can expand into softer tar (1)

(c) water could freeze, expand and crack the edges of the sections (1)

10.5 (i) boiling or evaporation (1)
(ii) melting (1)
(iii) freezing (1)
(iv) condensation (1)

10.6 (i) $34 \text{ cm}^3 - 30 \text{ cm}^3 = 4 \text{ cm}^3$ (2)
(ii) $124 \text{ g} - 80 \text{ g} = 44 \text{ g}$ (1)
(iii) density = mass/volume; $\frac{44}{4} = 11$ g per cm^3 (2)
(iv) the brooch is not silver, but it could contain silver as an alloy with lead (1)

10.7 (i) the force of the air particles against the inside wall of the tyre (1)
(ii) there are more particles, so they are closer together (1)
(iii) pressure increases, as particles move faster as they have absorbed heat energy (1)
(iv) particles of air can move around and so be pushed together solid rubber does not allow particles to move so easily (1)

10.8 (a) air-filled balloons are heavier than air, but helium-filled balloons are lighter than air (1)

(b) (i) A (1)
(ii) C (1)

(c) (i) diffusion (1)
(ii) particles are small enough to move between particles that make up the balloon wall (1)

22

11: Mixtures, separation and solubility

11.1 (a)   a compound   (1)

(b)   a suspension   (1)

(c)   evaporation   (1)

(d)   decanting   (1)

(e)   air   (1)

11.2 (a)   some substance in the stain is soluble in ethanol   (2)

(b)   (i)   chromatography   (1)
      (ii)   red; dark blue; yellow; pale blue   (1)
      (iii) two (two 'spots')   (1)
      (iv)   solute   (1)

11.3 (a)   (i)   mass of salt   (1)
      (ii)   boiling point of solution   (1)
      (iii) Both volume of water and type of salt dissolved in water must be controlled.
             Starting temperature of water and room temperature have little or no
             effect on results (either of these is a correct answer).   (3)

(b)   (i)   (3)

(ii)   about 107.5 °C   (1)

(iii) the gradient of the curve is 9.0 ÷ 60 = 1.5 °C per 10 g salt

100 g salt will raise the boiling point by 100 ÷ 10 × 1.5 = 15 °C

the boiling point of water is 100 °C

100 + 15 = 115 °C (2)

11.4 (a) (i) change in colour of the water (1)

(ii) raise temperature (1)

(b) evaporate the potassium manganate solution (1)

(c) (i) 14 g (1)

(ii) X (1)

(iii) X and Y (1)

11.5 concentrated – a solution with many solute particles in a small volume of solvent

saturated – a solution that cannot accept any more solute

solution – a mixture of a solvent and a solute; solvent – the liquid part of a solution

solubility – the amount of a substance that will dissolve in a liquid

soluble – able to dissolve (3)

11.6 (a) (i) kept same temperature; same volume of water (2)

(ii) curry powder (1)

(iii) 88 ÷ 32 = 2.8 (3)

(b) the water is very hot, and solubility depends on temperature (1)

11.7 (a) (i) fractional distillation (1)

(ii) evaporation then condensation (1)

(b) if liquid is water, anhydrous copper sulphate will turn from white to blue and cobalt chloride will turn from blue to pink; if liquid is pure water it will boil at 100 °C (2)

(c) (i) greater than 20 °C (1)

(ii) heat has been transferred from the steam (1)

(iii) it is cooled; particles get closer together/condensed (2)

11.8 (a) C (1)

(b) B (1)

(c) A (1)

(d) D (1)

12: Acids, bases and indicators

12.1 (a) corrosive (1)

(b) an acid (1)

(c) a neutralisation (1)

(d) neutral (1)

(e) a salt (1)

(f) a carbonate (1)

(g) carbon dioxide (1)

(h) salt + hydrogen (1)

(i) litmus paper blue (1)

(j) lactic acid (1)

12.2 (a) (i) red/orange (1)
    (ii) 2 (1)

(b) (i) | hydrochloric acid | + | magnesium carbonate | → | carbon dioxide | + | magnesium chloride | + | water | (2)

(ii) release of the gas carbon dioxide (1)
(iii) the acid was now the limiting factor
      no more acid to react with the magnesium carbonate (1)

(c) a salt; a compound (2)

12.3 (a) (i) methane; air (no change in colour of Universal Indicator) (2)
    (ii) carbon dioxide (most alkali needed to return solution to neutral) (2)
    (iii) neutralisation (1)

(b) (i) copper + hydrochloric acid → copper chloride + hydrogen (1)
    (ii) bronze is an alloy containing copper
        the copper reacts with the acid in the air
        copper salt is green (4)

12.4 (a) (2)

	acid or alkaline	colour of indicator solution
wasp sting	alkaline	greeny-blue
bee sting	acid	yellow

(b) (i) vinegar (1)
    (ii) bicarbonate toothpaste or baking soda (1)

(c) helps to sterilise teeth

helps to neutralise acidic foods, which are likely to damage teeth (2)

(d) (i) dock leaves release an alkali which neutralises the formic acid (1)

    (ii) relief is quicker if leaves are crushed because this releases alkali from the cells (1)

12.5 (a)

| calcium carbonate | + | hydrochloric acid | → | calcium chloride | + | carbon dioxide | + | water | (1) |

(b) loss of carbon dioxide (1)

(c) no more fizzing (1)

(d) green (1)

(e) marble; limestone; chalk (3)

(f) (i) hydrogen (1)

    (ii) hold lighted splint over the top of the mouth of the test tube in which the reaction is taking place; hydrogen will produce a 'pop' (1)

12.6 (a) C (1)

(b) A; B; D (1)

(c) E; F (1)

(d) neutralisation (1)

12.7 (a) it is very soluble in water; it is not poisonous (2)

(b) carbon dioxide is released; these bubbles make the cake lighter (1)

13: Elements and compounds

13.1 (a) is not usually dull in appearance (1)

(b) an element (1)

(c) moving slightly (1)

(d) an oxide (1)

(e) –ate (1)

13.2 (a) (i) D (1)
(ii) A (1)
(iii) D (1)
(iv) C, F (1)
(v) D (1)

13.3 (a) (3)

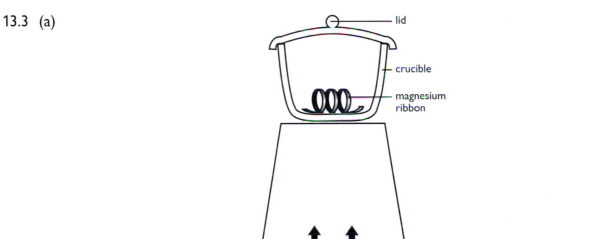

(b) (i) magnesium oxide (1)

(ii) (4)

a line of best fit (above) is ideal but connecting points with straight lines is also acceptable

(iii) 4.4/4.5 g   (1)
(iv) 9.6/9.7 g   (1)
(v) they are related, i.e. mass of oxide formed depends on mass of
magnesium available   (2)

13.4 (a) aluminium in saucepans – it is a good conductor of heat
silver for a necklace – it stays shiny because it does not react with oxygen in air
mercury in a barometer – it stays liquid at room temperature
helium in a balloon – it is lighter than air
copper in cables – it conducts electricity and is easy to stretch   (5)

(b) (i) Any two of:
good conductor of heat
easily made into correct shape
has high melting point   (2)
(ii) it is a gas so can be compressed into liquid form   (1)

13.5 (a) E   (1)

(b) B   (1)

(c) Mg; Cl   (2)

(d) iron sulphide   (1)

(e) (i) calcium hydroxide   (1)
(ii) greeny-blue   (1)
(iii) it is not an element   (1)

13.6 (a) (i) A   (1)
(ii) E   (1)

(b) Either: a compound contains only one type of molecule
or: a compound has fixed number of atoms   (1)

(c) (i) Any of: oxygen (O_2), hydrogen (H_2), chlorine (Cl_2)
or: other diatomic molecule (molecule with two atoms)   (1)
(ii) most likely answers are helium (He) and oxygen (O_2)   (2)

13.7 (a) it has a high melting point; it is a good conductor of heat and electricity   (2)

(b) (i) filtration   (1)
(ii) evaporation   (1)
(iii) chlorine; oceanium chloride   (2)

28

14: Chemical reactions

14.1 (a) the reaction being reversible (1)

(b) glucose (1)

(c) copper (1)

(d) carbon dioxide + water (1)

(e) decomposition (1)

(f) corrosion (1)

(g) releases heat (1)

(h) neutralisation (1)

(i) wood (1)

(j) adding extra water (1)

14.2 (a) (i) nitric acid + ammonium hydroxide → ammonium nitrate + water (1)
(ii) neutralisation (1)

(b) (i) 0–30 s (1)
(ii) 75% of 240 g (0.75 × 240) = 180 g; 240 − 180 = 60 g; time to reduce
to 60 g = 80 s (2)

14.3 (a) (i) iron + sulphur → iron sulphide (1)
(ii) loss of magnetic properties means that new product has been formed (1)

(b) (i) zinc sulphide (ZnS) (2)
(ii) sulphur + oxygen → sulphur dioxide (1)
(iii) it is an oxidation (1)

14.4 (a) (i) danger of damage to retina/eye (1)
(ii) remove any magnesium oxide from the surface (1)

(b) (i) 50; 62; 70 (1)
(ii) formation of magnesium oxide so a gain in mass equivalent to the
oxygen consumed in the reaction (2)
(iii) magnesium + oxygen → magnesium oxide (1)

14.5 (a) (i) source of methane – paddy fields/cattle ranches/rubbish tips
name of gas – carbon dioxide
percentage overall contribution to the greenhouse effect – 54% (2)
(ii) ensure that infrared radiation is shown reflected from Earth and then
back from layer of greenhouse gases (2)

(b) Any three of:
     stormy weather
     raised sea levels
     spreading of pests
     flooding
     formation of deserts   (3)

(c) (i)   Any two of: coal/oil/natural gas   (1)
     (ii) sulphur dioxide   (1)

(d) (i)   the pH will be raised   (1)
     (ii) calcium sulphate   (1)
     (iii) calcium hydroxide + sulphuric acid → calcium sulphate + water   (1)

14.6 (a) (i)   (3)

time (minutes)	volume of resin mix (cm³)
0	24
5	33
10	42
15	64
20	73
25	73
30	72

(ii)   (2)

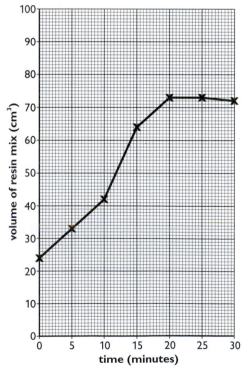

(iii) between 13 and 14 minutes   (1)

30

(b) (i) quantity of hardener (1)

    (ii) volume of resin mix (1)

    (iii) temperature; quantities of resin components (2)

(c) they must not deteriorate when in the air, or when they get wet during use (1)

15: The reactions of metals

15.1 (a) displacement (1)

(b) iron is oxidised and copper is reduced (1)

(c) silver (1)

(d) decomposition (1)

(e) iron (1)

15.2 (a) (i) type of metal (1)
(ii) volume of gas released (1)
(iii) by counting the bubbles (1)
(iv) same volume of acid; same-sized pieces of metal (2)

(b) In order of most to least reactive: magnesium, zinc, iron, copper (1)

(c) (i) no bubbles (1)
(ii) gold is very unreactive (1)

15.3 (a) (i) carbon monoxide + iron oxide → iron + carbon dioxide (1)
(ii) below (1)

(b) (i) 4.0 − 0.4 = 3.6; 3.6 ÷ 4.0 = 90% (2)
(ii) does not corrode (1)

(c) (i) 0.8% (1)
(ii) high carbon steel (1)

15.4 (a) (i) displacement (1)
(ii) magnesium + copper sulphate → magnesium sulphate + copper (2)

(b) (i) (1)

metal added to copper sulphate solution	starting temperature (°C)	final temperature (°C)	rise in temperature (°C)
magnesium	21.5	84.0	62.5
zinc	22.0	39.5	17.5
iron	23.0	34.5	11.5

(ii) from top to bottom: sodium, calcium, magnesium, aluminium, zinc, iron, lead, copper (1)
(iii) they are close together in the reactivity series (1)
(iv) For calcium and zinc sulphate, yes; for the other mixtures, no. (3)

15.5 (a) (i) bar = 0 (because layer of oil prevents air reaching nail) (2)

(ii) warmth had a bigger effect than salt – the nail in tube 3 (warm water only) rusted more than the nail in tube 2 (salt only) (2)

(b) (i) acidic (1)

(ii) hydrogen (1)

(iii) hold lighted splint over the top of the mouth of the test tube in which the reaction is taking place; hydrogen will produce a 'pop' (1)

(c) (i) acts as a barrier and also as a sacrificial metal (2)

(ii) it adds weight (1)

15.6 (a) (i) C (1)

(ii) B (1)

(iii) low down in column 2 (1)

(b) it is not an element (1)

(c) (i) iron + silver nitrate → iron nitrate + silver (2)

(ii) (4)

salt solution	metal			
	copper	iron	magnesium	zinc
iron nitrate	X	X	✓	X
zinc nitrate	X	X	✓	X
calcium nitrate	X	X	X	X

(d) gold is very unreactive so does not form an oxide (dull) with oxygen from the air; aluminium is more reactive (1)

Physics

16: Energy sources and transformations

16.1 (a) an iron   (1)

     (b) kinetic energy   (1)

     (c) joule   (1)

     (d) hydro   (1)

     (e) gravitational potential   (1)

16.2 (a) (i)   walls   (1)
         (ii) loss through walls is 35% of 10 000 (0.35 × 10 000) = 3500 J, so a 75% saving (0.75 × 3500) would reduce this by 2625 J; 10 000 − 2625 = 7375 J   (3)
         (iii) conductor; air; sound energy   (3)

     (b) layer of flexible material prevents heat transfer through the gap by convection   (2)

16.3 (a) (i)   sunlight   (1)
         (ii) solar energy causes thermal gradients, and air moves down these gradients causing winds; these can then drive wind turbines   (2)
         (iii) renewable   (1)

     (b) coal; gas; petrol is also acceptable (derived from a fossil fuel)   (2)

     (c) wood; photosynthesis; chemical; machine; heat   (2)

16.4 (a) potential; kinetic; light   (3)

     (b) more conversion of potential energy to kinetic energy is necessary to provide the extra light energy to make the lamp brighter   (1)

16.5 (a) (i) (4)

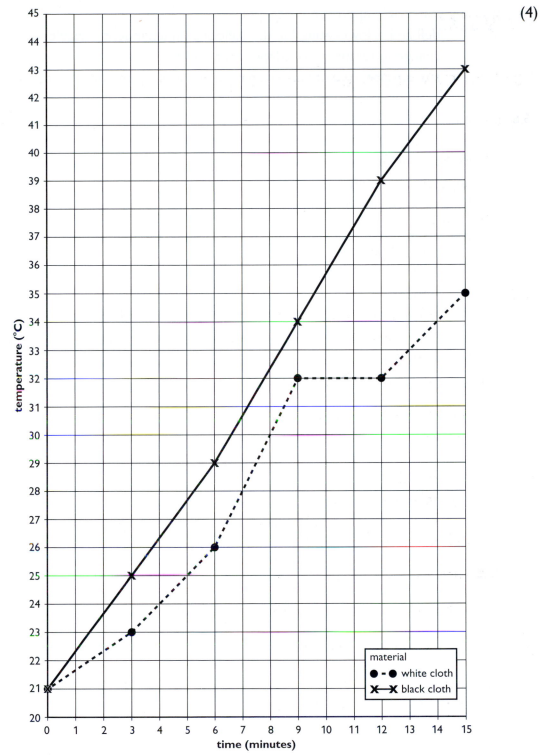

(ii) white cloth at 9 minutes (1)

(iii) the one covered in black cloth (1)

(iv) to keep this as a fixed (controlled) variable so that the investigation
is a fair test (1)

(b) any reasonable approach is acceptable:
dull and shiny coating for the balloons (independent variable)
change in temperature (dependent variable)
size/surface area of balloon, temperature of room and type of
thermometer used (controlled variables)   (4)

16.6 (a) coal – generating electricity in power stations
natural gas – heating and cooking in homes
petrol – fuel for cars
kerosene – aircraft fuel
butane – cooking on camping stoves   (2)

(b) the quantity of a non-renewable fuel gets less as it is used up   (1)

(c) (i) a fuel made originally by photosynthesis   (1)
(ii) sunlight energy   (1)
(iii) Either of: fossil fuels are reliable; are very concentrated stores of energy   (1)

16.7 (a) D, E, B, A, C   (2)

(b) (i)   (4)

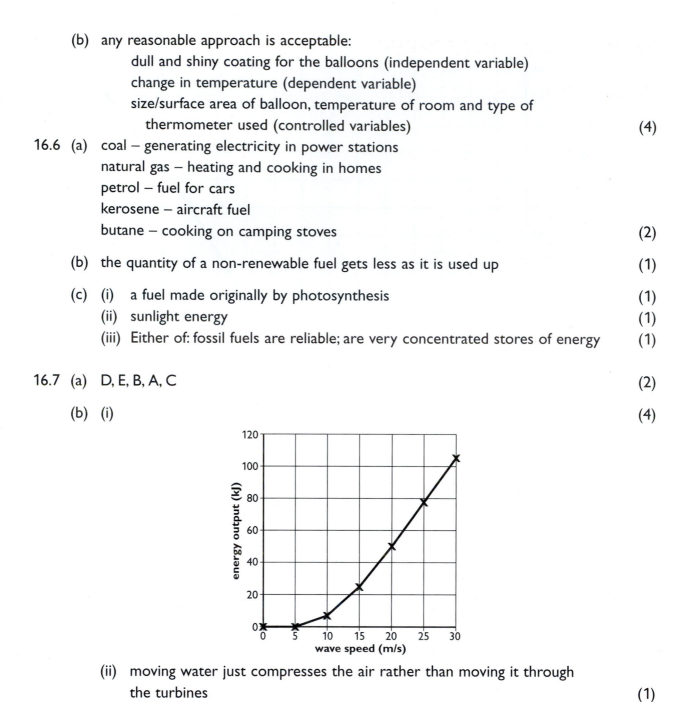

(ii) moving water just compresses the air rather than moving it through
the turbines   (1)

17: Electricity and energy

17.1 (a) turbine   (1)

(b) battery   (1)

(c) graphite   (1)

(d) TV monitor   (1)

(e) generator   (1)

17.2 (a) (i)   58%   (1)
(ii) 35%   (1)
(iii) heat   (1)

(b) (i)   lumo 17.3; glo-bright 16; eco-save 18; brite-lite 20; supa-glow 18.3   (1)
(ii)   (3)

bars must not be touching

(iii) brand of bulb   (1)
(iv) brightness of bulb   (1)
(v) same power supply; length of warm-up time; distance from sensor   (3)
(vi) repeated readings/checked each other's readings/calculated means   (1)
(vii) that not all bulbs are equally efficient in conversion of electrical energy
to light energy   (1)

17.3 (i)   chemical; kinetic; electrical; light; heat   (3)
(ii) the battery is able to store electrical energy, so the lights will stay
bright even if the dynamo is not turning (e.g. when the engine is
turned off)   (2)

17.4 (a) (i) panels were not always facing towards the Sun to the same extent (2)

(ii) 6 hours (8 to 14 on the graph) (1)

(iii) (2)

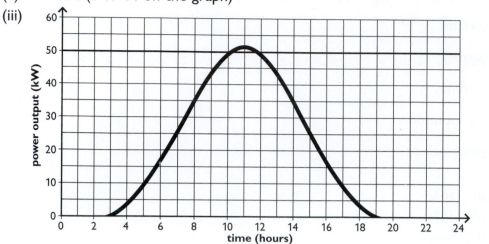

same height but more spread, i.e. at maximum for much longer
(effectively for 24 hours unless satellite in shadow)

(b) it means that the spacecraft does not need to carry another form of
fuel, which would be very heavy (1)

17.5 (a) all correct for five marks, lose 1 mark for each incorrect label:
A – fuel input; B – boiler; C – cooling tower; D – electricity output;
E – generator; F – turbine; G – steam jet; H – furnace (5)

(b) (i) In gigajoules per tonne: coal 39; oil 36; gas 51; nuclear 42 (4)

(ii) Any two of:
smoke is harmful
production of greenhouse gases
coal is non-renewable (2)

(iii) advantage – it does not produce pollutants
disadvantage – it is less reliable since winds are not consistent in strength (2)

17.6 (a) advantages – any two of:
easy to transfer along power lines
no waste
easily transformed to other energy form
easy to control delivery
disadvantages – any two of:
cannot be stored in large quantities
transfer requires high voltages, so can be dangerous (2)

(b) (i) Test each insulator in turn by attaching the clips to either end and
measuring the current that flows using the ammeter. More efficient
insulators allow less current to flow. (2)

(ii) Any one of:
      battery always supplies the same power
      same clips and wires offer the same resistance
      same thickness of insulator samples   (1)
(iii) any sensible example, e.g. plastic as body of plugs to prevent
      electric shocks   (2)

18: Electrical circuits

18.1 (a) an electron (1)

(b) cell (1)

(c) volt (1)

(d) switch (1)

(e) amp (1)

(f) a conductor (1)

(g) series circuit (1)

(h) a resistor (1)

(i) shine more brightly (1)

(j) parallel circuit (1)

18.2 (a) A – switch; B – bulb; C – cells/battery; D – ammeter; E – resistor (5)

(b) (i) the battery (1)
(ii) the ammeter (1)
(iii) (2)

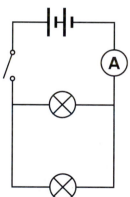

(c) copper (1)

18.3 (a) E (1)

(b) (2)

switch A	switch B	bulb X	bulb Y	bulb Z
open	open	off	off	off
closed	open	off	off	off
open	closed	on	off	on

(c) all show 0.6 amps (1)

18.4 (a) (i)   the circuit was completed when the switch contacts were pushed
                 together   (1)
           (ii)   (3)

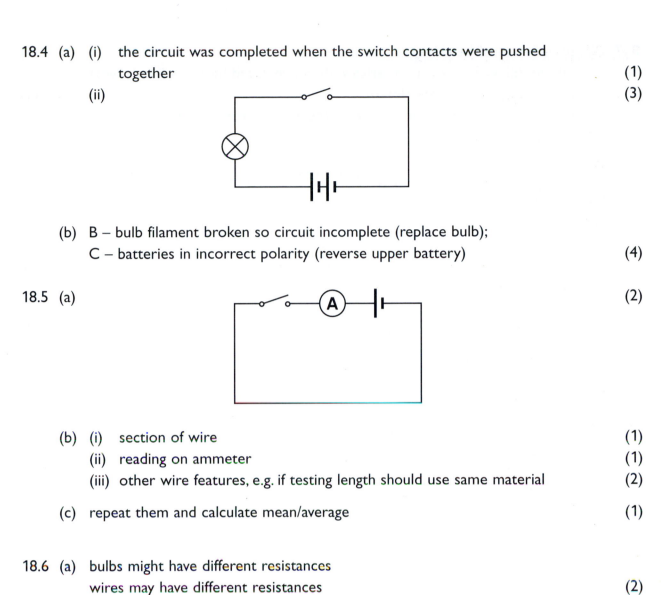

       (b) B – bulb filament broken so circuit incomplete (replace bulb);
            C – batteries in incorrect polarity (reverse upper battery)   (4)

18.5 (a)   (2)

       (b) (i)   section of wire   (1)
            (ii) reading on ammeter   (1)
            (iii) other wire features, e.g. if testing length should use same material (2)

       (c) repeat them and calculate mean/average   (1)

18.6 (a) bulbs might have different resistances
           wires may have different resistances   (2)

       (b)   (1)

       (c)   (2)

measured current (amps)

time (hours)

18.7 (a) (i) both must be closed (1)

(ii) no (blower motor is in series with switch 1, and heater will only work
if both switches are closed). (1)

(iii) it will still work, although it will receive more current (so may
become hotter) (1)

(b) (1)

position of switch 1	position of switch 2	bulb on or off?
B	D	on
A	D	off
A	C	on

(c) (i) neither is on (1)

(ii) nothing happens to bulb Y (1)

19: Magnetic fields and electromagnetism

19.1 (a) poles (1)

 (b) copper (1)

 (c) both force and direction (1)

 (d) resistance of the wire (1)

 (e) solenoid (1)

19.2 (a) results: repel; nothing happens
 conclusions: X is steel; Y is the magnet; Z is copper (3)

 (b) (2)

 (c) compass needle aligned with lines of force, pointing south (1)

 (d) magnetic field; attracted; North-seeking; repelled (3)

19.3 (a) the switch is open so the circuit is incomplete and the electromagnet
 cannot attract the armature (2)

 (b) switch closed → electromagnet pulls on armature → armature moves so
 gong strikes bell → contact breaker breaks the circuit → spring pushes
 armature back again so circuit is complete and the sequence can start
 all over again (5)

19.4 (a) current; material of coiled wire; number of turns in coiled wire (3)

 (b) (i) coil becomes an electromagnet and so 'pulls' on the iron disc (2)
  (ii) 1.0 (glass has no effect as a core material) (1)

19.5 (a) (i) the current may not have been great enough to cause the (2)
   electromagnet to pull on the movable strip in the reed
  (ii) increase number of coils; increase current (2)

 (b) opening the door moves the magnet away from the normally-closed
 reed switch; this allows the contacts to meet and the alarm bell
 circuit to be completed (2)

19.6 (a) (5)

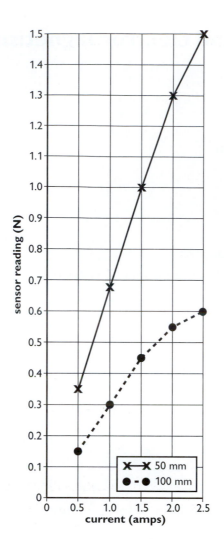

(b) (i)   increasing the current increases the strength (1)

(ii) Any two of:
insert an iron core
increase number of coils in coiled wire
reduce resistance of coiled wire (2)

(c) circuit completed as switch closed; electromagnet 'pulls' on iron
counterweight; barrier lifts (2)

19.7 (a) (i)   same number of paper clips is picked up by each of them (1)

(ii) with iron as the core the electromagnet is clearly 'on' or 'off'; the steel
stays magnetised even when the current is 'off' (1)

(b) electromagnet will only pick up steel cans when switched on; steel
cans can be removed and aluminium cans can be left behind; steel cans
can be dropped elsewhere when the electromagnet is switched 'off' (2)

(c) (i)   large current makes electromagnet pull on steel catch; this releases
the contact, which pulls away because of the spring; circuit is now
incomplete so current no longer flows (2)

(ii) it can be reset by pushing down on the reset button; an ordinary fuse
must be replaced (1)

20: Heat and energy

20.1 (a) conduction (1)

(b) Kelvin scale (1)

(c) kinetic energy (1)

(d) joule (1)

(e) radiation (1)

(f) 36.9 °C (1)

(g) evaporation (1)

(h) a good thermal insulator (1)

(i) convection (1)

(j) useful energy output with energy input (1)

20.2 (a) (i) fox B lives in Greenland (smaller ears limit heat loss); fox A lives in Kenya (larger ears provide a greater surface area for heat loss) (2)

(ii) heat transfer to the soil by conduction (1)

(b) (i) Any two of:
same volume of hot water
both tests starting at the same temperature
cans made of the same material
measurements taken at same time intervals (2)

(ii) (4)

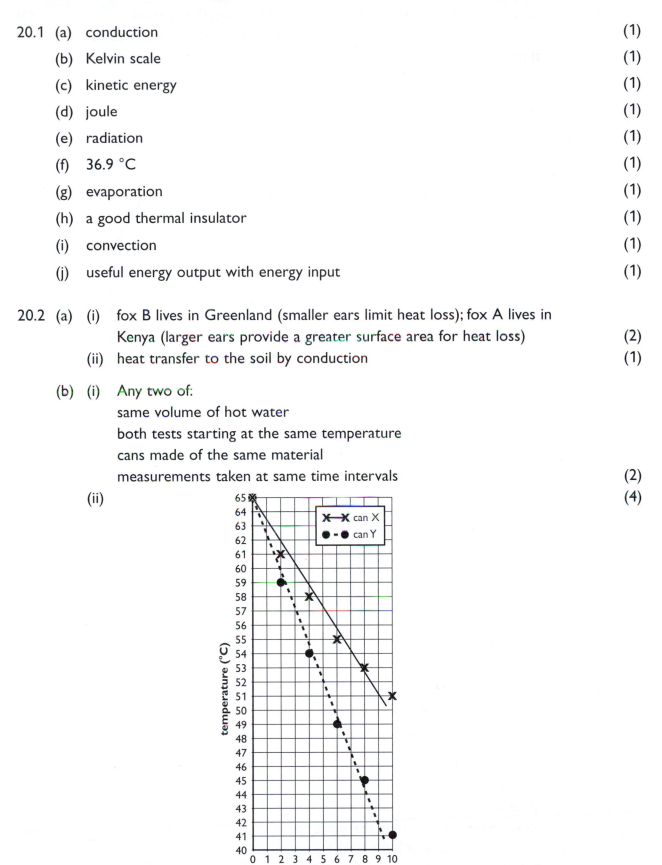

a line of best fit (above) is ideal but connecting points with straight lines is also acceptable

45

(iii) results support (a) (i) because bigger flaps lose heat more quickly (2)

(c) (i) heat loss is slower, so less heat loss over the same time period (1)
(ii) he should have performed the experiment with flaps out at the same time as flaps flat, as room temperature could have changed and that would have altered the rate of heat loss (2)

20.3 (a) (i) conduction (1)
(ii) particles gain energy from heat and vibrate more, passing on their energy to other particles nearby (1)

(b) (i) (2)

immersion heater

warmer water is less dense so moves upwards (convection)

heat transferred to gravel (conduction)

heat transferred to cooler water (conduction)

(ii) particles in brass rod cannot move as much as molecules in water (1)
(iii) radiation (1)

(c) (i) evaporation (1)
(ii) it will fall (1)
(iii) the particles with the most energy have escaped so the ones left behind have less energy and so are cooler (1)

20.4 (a) (i) type of food (1)
(ii) temperature of water (1)
(iii) Any two of:
volume of water
mass of food sample
same thermometer
experiment performed in the same room (2)
(iv) 1 g of fat contains 38500 J, so 0.2 g contains 38500 ÷ 5 = 7700 J;
7700 J can raise the temperature of 25 cm³ of water by
(7700 ÷ 4.2) ÷ 25 = 73 °C (3)

46

      (v) Any two of:
           some might be carried away on air currents (lost to the environment)
           some is lost as light energy
           some is used to warm up the glass and not the water   (2)

  (b) (i)   thermal insulation   (1)
      (ii) they are thinner   (1)
     (iii) wrap them up in clothes to act as insulators   (1)

20.5 (i)   chemical; muscles; respiration; oxygen   (2)
     (ii) gravitational potential energy   (1)
    (iii) kinetic; gravitational potential   (1)
    (iv) kinetic; gravitational potential   (1)

21: The Earth and the Solar System

21.1 (a)   150 kg   (1)

   (b)   the Earth lies between the Sun and the Moon   (1)

   (c)   star   (1)

   (d)   lunar month   (1)

   (e)   they reflect light from the Sun   (1)

   (f)   the Moon is smaller than the Earth   (1)

   (g)   Venus   (1)

   (h)   much faster   (1)

   (i)   geostationary   (1)

   (j)   light years   (1)

21.2 (a)   (2)

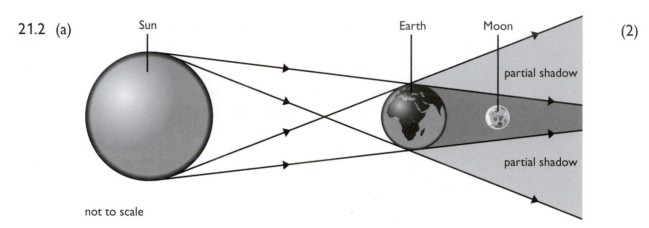

not to scale

any one label incorrect loses 1 mark

   (b)   Birds use the amount of light to decide when to sing or be more active.
         Some birds became less active at night during a lunar eclipse. (All birds stop
         singing during a total solar eclipse.)   (1)

   (c)   (3)

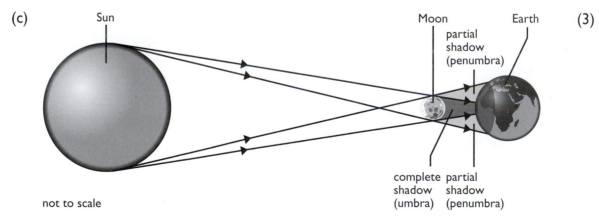

not to scale

any one label incorrect loses 1 mark

   (d)   31st July 1981   (2)

48

21.3 luminous; constellations; galaxy; telescope; light years; Milky Way (3)

21.4 (a) transmitter must be able to reflect microwaves from satellite
reflected waves to be picked up by receiver
lines of reflection must be straight lines (2)

geostationary satellite

(b) (i) if not, transmitted waves would not be reflected to the receiver (1)
    (ii) one day/24 hours (1)
    (iii) gravity (1)
    (iv) signals only travel in straight lines, i.e. a signal can only travel from a transmitter to a satellite if the satellite is above the horizon; having several satellites in different positions ensures that some are always above the horizon (2)

(c) Moon; any planet (Earth most likely) (2)

21.5 one year on Earth is 365 days – the Earth orbits the Sun
at the Equator, there are 12 hours of light and 12 hours of darkness – the Earth rotates on its axis
in Britain there are four seasons in the year – the Earth's axis is tilted
there is a new Moon every month – the Moon orbits the Earth
a ship sailing away from land goes out of sight – the Earth is a sphere (5)

21.6 (a) (i) D (1)
    (ii) B (1)
    (iii) A (1)
    (iv) G (1)

(b) (i) all arrows pointing towards centre of the Moon (1)
    (ii) collecting bag on chain always pointing towards the centre of the Moon (1)

(c) (i) the Earth orbits the Sun because the superior gravitational force of
the Sun holds the smaller Earth at a distance as it moves (2)
(ii) one year/365 days (1)
(iii) 149 000 000 (distance) ÷ 300 000 (speed) = 496.7 (time in seconds);
496.7 ÷ 60 (number of seconds in minute) = just over 8 minutes or 480 s (2)

21.7 (a) (i) it is in an orbit in a different plane to the other planets (1)
(ii) planets often have natural moons; Charon is acting like a moon
around the planet Pluto (1)

(b) (i) (1)

(ii) greatest gravitational force close to the Sun (1)

22: Forces and linear motion

22.1 (a) 7.5 cm^3 (1)

    (b) distance/time   (1)

    (c) newton   (1)

    (d) all forces on it are balanced   (1)

    (e) a size and a direction   (1)

22.2 (a) (i)   run 5   (1)

         (ii) 6.13 s   (1)

         (iii) it reduces the effect of any one result, which could be unrepresentative   (1)

    (b) (i) $\text{speed} = \dfrac{\text{distance travelled}}{\text{time taken}}$ (1)

         (ii) 500 m ÷ 6.13 s = 81.6 m/s   (2)

    (c) the air resistance/wind resistance was different in the two directions   (1)

22.3 (a) X – upthrust; Y – gravity   (2)

    (b) friction of water
friction of air/air resistance/drag   (2)

    (c) stabiliser angled downwards, i.e. front end below rear end   (1)

22.4 (a) (i)   it reduces wind resistance/air resistance/drag   (1)

         (ii) friction   (1)

         (iii) it has very little friction on the track surface   (1)

(b) (i)

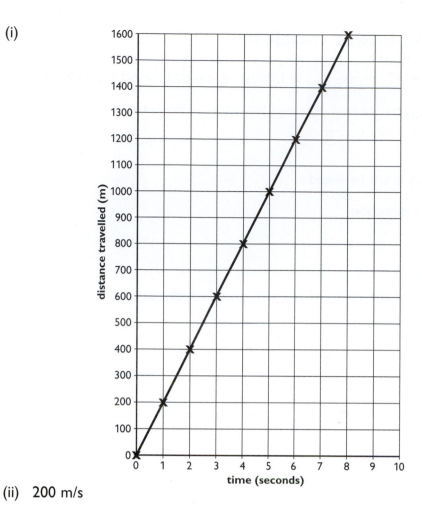

    (ii) 200 m/s   (1)
    (iii) 700 m   (1)
    (iv) 600 m   (1)
    (v) 12.5 s   (1)

22.5 (a) (i) at mass of 400 g   (1)
      (ii) 430 g; 2.4 N   (2)

    (b) gravity; mass; number; type   (2)

    (c) (i) gravitational force is lower in space so the forces to overcome
          gravity are also lower   (2)
      (ii) arrow upwards diagonally to the right   (1)

22.6 (a) (i) liquid is denser so takes up much less volume for the same mass of fuel   (2)
      (ii) no oxygen in space, but plenty in Earth's atmosphere/on Earth's surface   (1)

    (b) (i) thrust (upwards), gravity (downwards)   (2)
      (ii) weight of rocket and fuel is greater than the thrust at 20 s   (1)
      (iii) upward force = 54 million N; total weight = 36 million N; resultant
           force = 54 − 36 = 18 million N upwards   (1)
      (iv) fuel is being burned   (1)

22.7 (a) (i) 19 minutes   (1)

(ii)   between C and D   (1)

(iii) B to C/E to F   (1)

(iv)   4 km ÷ 19 minutes = 0.21 km per minute; 0.21 × 60 = 12.6 km per hour   (2)

(b) (i)   to increase friction between feet and mud/prevent slipping   (1)

     (ii) chemical; kinetic; heat   (1)

23: Friction and motion

23.1 (a) moment (1)

    (b) centre of gravity (1)

    (c) pascal (1)

    (d) drag (1)

    (e) newton-metre (1)

23.2 (a) (i) allow 1 mark for the number and 1 mark for the unit:
           0.5 m × 1000 N = 500 Nm (2)
      (ii) 500 Nm ÷ 0.8 m = 625 N (1)

    (b) to increase friction between tyres and mud/prevent slipping (1)

    (c) (i) to provide a small surface area so that pressure applied to the log
will be very high (1)
      (ii) allow 1 mark for the correct number and 1 mark for the appropriate unit:
           600 N ÷ 1.2 cm² = 500 N per cm² = 500 ÷ 10 000 =
           0.05 N per m² (pascals) (2)

23.3 (a) (i) increase surface area so decrease pressure and so less chance of
falling through crust of snow (2)
      (ii) bristles – increase friction/prevent slipping
fur-like hairs – thermal insulation/limit heat loss by conduction (2)

    (b) lubricant; friction (1)

23.4 (a) (i) down (1)
      (ii) up (1)

    (b) mass = 12 kg so weight = 120 N and turning moment = 120 × 2 m = 240 Nm (2)

    (c) (i) pivot is at joint between upper and lower jaws (1)
      (ii) reduced distance to pivot means that greater force can be applied
to fruit for less effort expended (2)

23.5 (a) (i) any weight on the baseboard would apply a turning moment to the
board around the edge of the old desk (2)
      (ii) the mass of the board itself (1)

    (b) (i) 5 N × 0.2 m = 1.0 Nm (2)
      (ii) for balanced forces the moment of the boxes must = 1 Nm
= 10 N × 0.1 m, i.e. weight of boxes = 10 N (2)
      (iii) oil/some suitable lubricant (fills in cavities so reduces friction between
the surfaces) (2)

23.6 (a) (i) forcemeter (1)

(ii) to prevent the trolley sliding without any effort being applied
(otherwise may not get any reading on forcemeter) (1)

(b) (i) type of material (1)

(ii) reading on forcemeter (1)

(iii) Any two of:
added mass
surface on which material is sliding
mass of trolley
use same forcemeter for each reading (2)

(iv) to allow the calculation of an average/mean (to make results
more reliable) (1)

(c) (i) P 2.0; Q 4.5; R 3.2; S 1.0; T 6.5 (2)

(ii) T (1)

(iii) S (1)

(iv) values would fall, as friction would be reduced (1)

23.7 (a) so that the turning moment does not cause it to tip over (1)

(b) (i) 3000 N × 5 m = 15 000 Nm (1)

(ii) 4500 N × 5 m = 22 500 Nm (1)

(iii) 22 500 Nm ÷ 10 000 N = 2.25 m (1)

(iv) 30 000 Nm = turning moment with counterweight maximum distance
from pivot; maximum load = 30 000 ÷ 5 m; maximum load = 6000 N (1)

24: Light

24.1 (a) the Moon (1)

    (b) opaque (1)

    (c) much more quickly (1)

    (d) retina (1)

    (e) in front of the mirror (1)

    (f) incidence is equal to the angle of reflection (1)

    (g) reflection (1)

    (h) red, blue and green (1)

    (i) dispersion (1)

    (j) transmits blue light (1)

24.2 (a) (i) red (1)
       (ii) the white letters reflected the red light (1)

    (b) (i) blue (1)
       (ii) black (1)
       (iii) the white letters reflected the blue light, and the top appeared black, as there was no blue pigment to reflect the blue light (1)

24.3 (a) (2)

    (b) (3)

(c) (i) white light from headlight beam reflects from multiple surfaces; whatever the angle of incidence, some light reflects back to eyes of driver (2)

(ii) would only reflect back if light from headlights hit mirror at 90° (1)

(iii) the material has a roughened surface which does not reflect the light in any organised way (1)

24.4 (a) refraction (1)

(b) dispersion (1)

(c) (i) only the red part of the spectrum would be seen (1)

(ii) other colours have been absorbed by the solution (2)

(iii) red would disappear, as there is no longer a red pigment to reflect the red light (2)

(d) beetles would appear black (red light is only reflected by red pigment, not blue or yellow); black beetles would be difficult to see at night! (2)

24.5 (a) light is reflected from the surface of the balls (which are smooth, so shiny) back to the eyes of the player (2)

(b) (i) only red balls would appear coloured – all others would appear to be black (1)

(ii) black ball is always black since the black colour absorbs all colours/wavelengths of light (1)

(c) because light travels in straight lines and so the area behind the ball does not receive light (1)

(d) snooker balls are smooth, so reflection will be 'clear', but table surface is rough, so reflection will be 'multi-angled' (2)

24.6 (a)   (2)

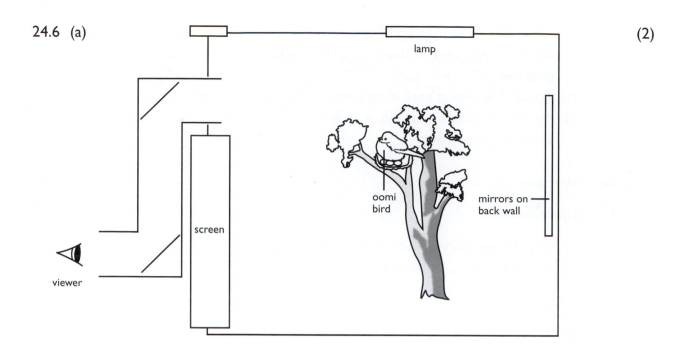

mirrors at 45° within periscope tube

(b)   (1)

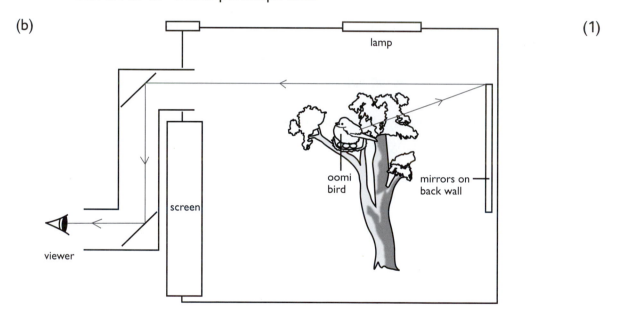

(c)   she only reflects green light, so the red light makes her look very dark   (1)

(3)

24.7 (i) refraction (1)

(ii) some light has been absorbed (1)

(iii) red; orange; yellow; green; blue; indigo; violet (1)

25: Vibration and sound

25.1 (a) plucking the string harder (1)

(b) much more slowly (1)

(c) eardrum (1)

(d) listen to a message on the phone (1)

(e) glass wall – aluminium frame – water – air (1)

(f) the nerve to the brain is damaged (1)

(g) cannot travel through a vacuum (1)

(h) amplitude (1)

(i) hertz (1)

(j) higher (1)

25.2 (a) (i) B and C (1)
      (ii) A and C (1)

(b) (i) vibration causes the eardrum to vibrate and it might tear or split (2)
      (ii) 89 db is half way between 88 and 90, so time is halfway between 2 and 4 h = 3.0 h (note logarithmic relationship between sound level and time) (2)

25.3 (a) (i) decibels (1)
      (ii) (4)

      (iii) polystyrene block (1)

(b) (i) type of material (1)
      (ii) sound detected by sensor (1)
      (iii) the distance between the sound sensor and the box (2)

25.4 (a) all must be correct for 2 marks/four correct for 1 mark:
A – pinna; B – ear canal; C – cochlea; D – nerve; E – ossicles; F – eardrum (2)

(b) (i) it vibrates (1)
(ii) electrical impulses/messages are transferred to the brain (1)

(c) (i) more than 50 000 Hz but less than 65 000 Hz (too high for robin and
dog but not too high for cat) (2)
(ii) the echo is reflected, so travels twice the distance, thus takes 0.1 s to
reach the shoal of fish which at 1500 m per s = 150 m (3)

25.5 (a) to prevent the bang tearing his eardrum/causing damage to his hearing (1)

(b) sound travels more slowly, so he would start the watch later
(this would give an apparently shorter time for the race) (2)

(c) the spectators could have heard the sound as it travelled directly from
the gun as well as an echo via the dining hall wall (2)

25.6 (a) (i) sound (vibrations) cannot travel through space/atmosphere on Moon (1)
(ii) vibration can travel through air in helmet and through solid material
of helmet (2)

(b) (i) light/solar energy (1)
(ii) electrical to chemical (1)

(c) P (1)

25.7 (a) (i) the bell rings when the circuit is completed (1)
(ii) the sound gradually disappears as the air is withdrawn from the bell,
and sound does not travel through a vacuum (1)

(b) (i) sound travels more slowly than light (1)
(ii) less than one second (1)

    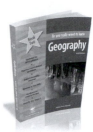